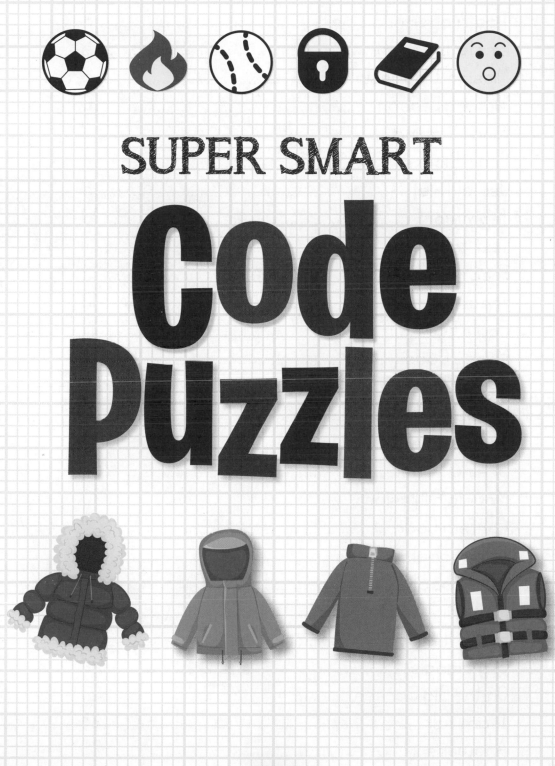

SUPER SMART
Code
Puzzles

ARCTURUS

CONTENTS

TIPS ON CODE PUZZLES FROM ANITA CLUE

Think outside the box! Don't just look for obvious solutions, but tackle the puzzle from a different angle.

Be logical! Work through a puzzle slowly, step by step.

Decode the message onto a separate piece of paper as you work it out.

Look for words in the introduction that might give clues to finding the solution.

PIRATE TREASURE

Help Captain Swashbuckle solve the secret message on the cave wall to discover where the treasure is hidden!

```
T H E T
S A E R
U R E L
B S E I
E N E A
H T H T
E G O L D
U K S N E L
L L
```

Agent 003½ is off on her next mission. Crack the code to find out what gear she will need this time!

I need **D+E**

Her next mission is:

A In the desert

B At sea

C In the mountains

HISTORY LESSON

Senator Misterius is here to share some fascinating facts about the Romans. Work out what the "X"s have replaced to read his secret scroll.

RXMXNS XTX
WXTH THXXR
HXNDS XND
NXVXR XSXD
X KNXFX
XR FXRK.

Mrs. Cipher is a teacher who loves setting puzzles for her class. Take the correct path through the maze to spell out what they will study today!

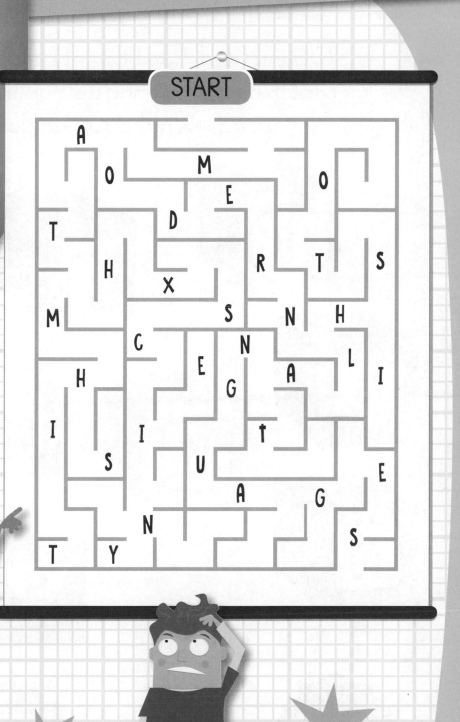

START

BUILDING BLOCKS

Granny Gumshoe has set Lucy a puzzle. Find the matching blocks, and pair up the letters to form words. What question do they make?

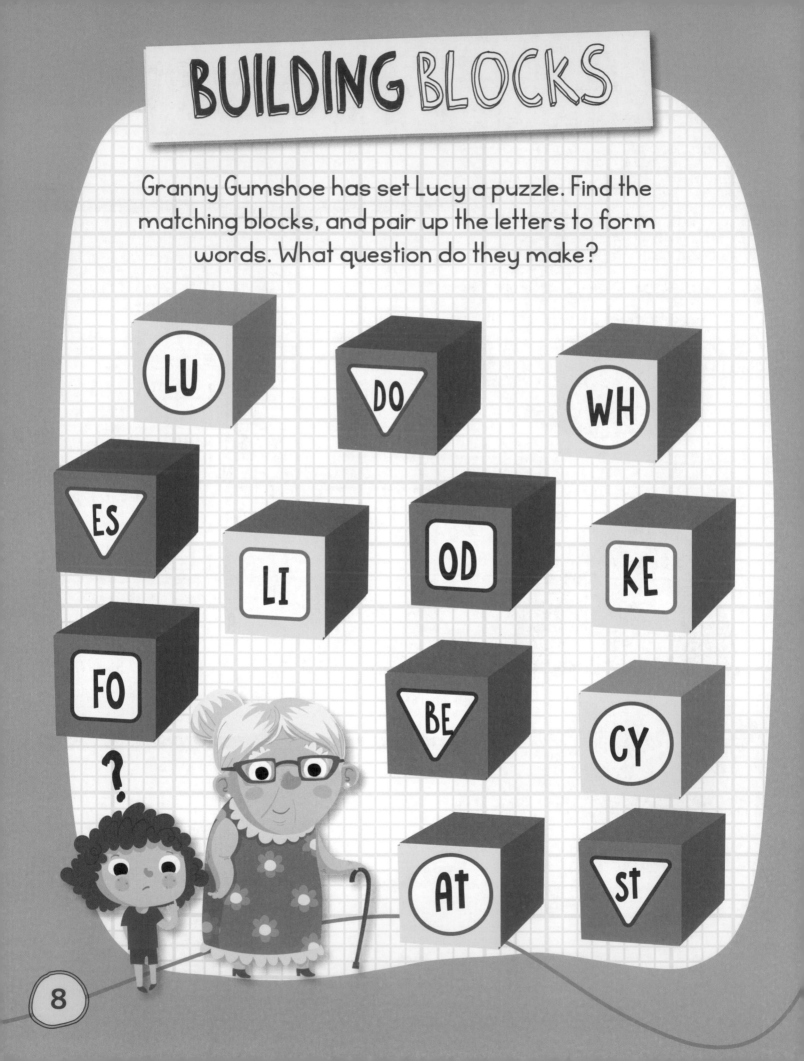

Rob Cash is trying to steal some jewels. But only nine of them are real! Where are they? They are arranged in the same pattern as in his picture.

TEAMWORK

Sanjay and Will have each received a coded message about the next meeting of Super Secret Club. What does it say?

Here's a clue: They will need to work together!

KIWI
FAME
NINE
ORCA
WIFI
PAPA
MONO

LLAMA
ETHIC
AROMA
FETCH
VERGE
STONE
ONION

text test

At first glance, these are just emojis gone crazy. But look for similar icons that can be joined with three straight lines to find the single emoji you should text to your contact. Hint:The arrow will point you in the right direction!

FEEDING TIME!

Riddle Raccoon has been on the rampage! Figure out what he has eaten this time, if A = 2, B = 3, C = 4 and so on.

7.16.16.5

7.19.16.14 21.9.6

5.16.8

3.16.24.13

TREASURE HUNT

Take a close look at the Captain's map.
What is the secret message hidden on it?

⚙	☠	❄	⚑	◎	💣	☀	❄	⊕	≈
A	D	E	I	G	N	R	T	2	3

Eagle Eyes Eddie can spot a code a mile away. Can you match his skills, and figure out what this message says?

i

b

a

h

t

y

h

r

P

t

o

o

P

a

d

y

u

y

14

MORSE CODE

Use this code of dots and dashes to help you solve cases with Anita Clue.

A •-
B -•••
C -•-•
D -••
E •
F ••-•
G --•
H ••••
I ••

J •---
K -•-
L •-••
M --
N -•
O ---
P •--•
Q --•-
R •-•

S •••
T -
U ••-
V •••-
W •--
X -••-
Y -•--
Z --••

••/-//••/•••//

•/•-/•••/-•--//-/---//

••-/•/•-/--•//---/---/•-•/•••/•//

-•-•/---/-••/•//

SECRET AGENT

What is the name of the master criminal that Sherlock Bones has to track down? Find the common letter on each line of names to spell it out.

Paige	Gabriel	Etienne	Kelly
Gideon	Anders	Sinead	Rashid
Dawn	Wendy	Rockwell	Werner
Edison	Lisbet	Gia	Felipe
Annika	Evan	Tristan	Leonie

Jet Setting

Paul R. Bear is on a mystery tour. If his first ticket is for a flight to Istanbul, what are the other secret destinations? Clue: They are all countries, not cities.

SECRET SPELLS

Find how many mice are hiding in the castle, and then count around the spell ring, circling that letter each time, to find the hidden ingredient for Bafflemore's potion.

Clue: If there are six mice, circle the sixth letter each time.

START HERE

SEEING DOUBLE

Claire has sent someone's name to Super Secret Club. Can you figure out who it is? The clue is "SEEING DOUBLE."

Crafty Claire

Tricky Tess

cabbage
borrow
aardvark
funny
middle
goose
cannon

Sneaky Sanjay

Wily Will

Start at the trees and follow the letters to find eight things needed on a trek into the mountains. The leftover letters will spell an extra treat you should take with you.

S A D D L E C R E I

t O O B R T A H A S N

S R C O A T O D R I N

E P O R S D O O F t K

CONFETTI CODE

Spot six differences between these two pictures. Use the six shapes that are different in the right-hand image to work out the code word.

SPOOOOOOKY!

SCOORY NOOOOSOOS KOOOOP MOOKOONG MOO JOOMP!

This ghost has brought a message from the other side! What is it trying to say?

22

LITTLE ROBOT

This little robot has a very special talent. What is it?

Clue: Look at the <u>orange</u> and <u>yellow</u> squares to find out!

T	L	R	A	A
N	N	G	S	U
L	A	A	G	T
E	I	S	N	+
G	+	+	+	+

Monster Munch

This monster loves the taste of sour cream salsa! Which snack should he choose?

What message does each of these pirate flags show?

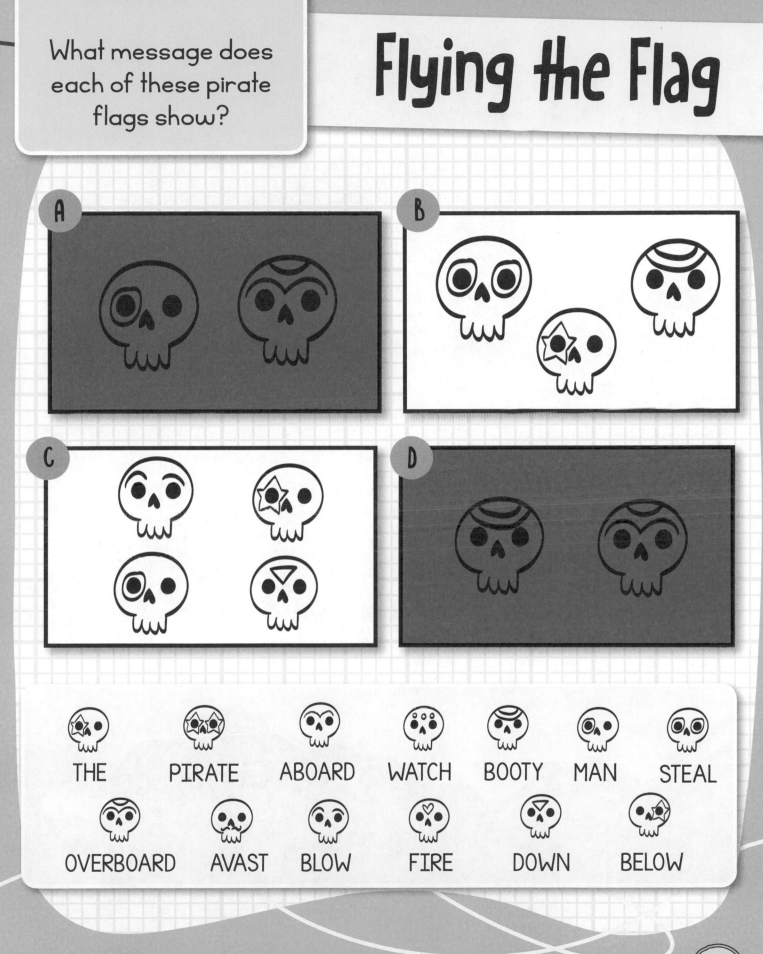

A

B

C

D

THE   PIRATE   ABOARD   WATCH   BOOTY   MAN   STEAL

OVERBOARD   AVAST   BLOW   FIRE   DOWN   BELOW

SKY SIGNALS

This grizzly has spotted a smoke message across the valley. What does it say?
(Turn to page 15 for the decoder.)

Super Secret Club is watching a movie in 3D, but first this message flashes on the screen. What does it say?

Clue: Red first

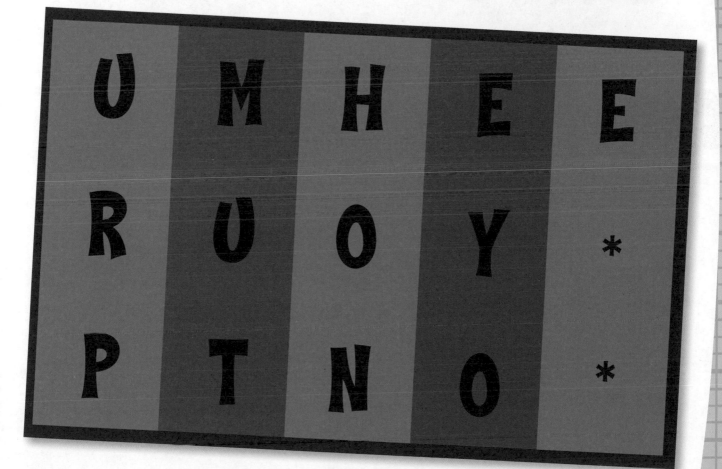

Which team do these cheerleaders support? Use their shirts to work it out.

☺	⌁	◉	✦	★	◆	♓	◎	❖
Y	R	E	K	B	N	W	A	O

Answers

4. Pirate Treasure
THE TREASURE LIES BENEATH
THE GOLDEN SKULL

5. Mission Impossible
B

6. History Lesson
Replace the Xs with the correct vowels
to get: ROMANS ATE WITH THEIR
HANDS AND NEVER USED A KNIFE
OR FORK

7. Mind Mapping

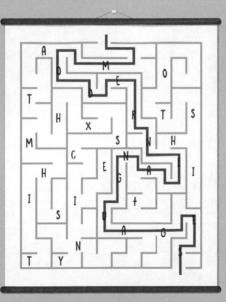

MODERN LANGUAGES

8. Building Blocks
WHAT FOOD DOES LUCY LIKE BEST?

9. Jewel Thief

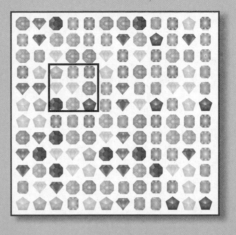

10. Teamwork
Read the underlined letters
together to get: WILL MEET BETH
NEAR CAFE NOON

11. Text Test

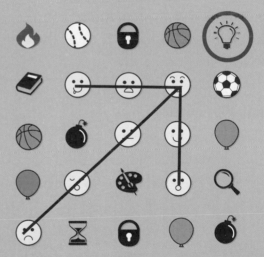

12. Feeding Time!
FOOD FROM THE DOG BOWL

13. Treasure Hunt
DIG IN D2

14. Eagle Eyes
Group together letters in the same style of writing to see: HAPPY BIRTHDAY TO YOU

15. Morse Code
IT IS EASY TO READ MORSE CODE

16. Secret Agent
EDWIN

17. Jet Setting
BULGARIA, BRAZIL, GHANA, THAILAND, TANZANIA

18. Secret Spells
There are three hidden mice, so circle every third letter to read: BAT BREATH

19. Seeing Double
Use one of the double letters that appear in each word to spell the name: BRANDON

20. Mountain Mission
You will need these items: SADDLE, REINS, HAT, BOOTS, COAT, DRINK, FOOD, ROPE. Don't forget the CARROTS for your trusty steed!

21. Confetti Code
The code word is: PURPLE

22. Spoooooooky!
Replace each OO with the correct vowel to see: SCARY NOISES KEEP MAKING ME JUMP!

23. Little Robot
TRANSLATING LANGUAGES

24. Monster Munch
The green packet. The others are salt and vinegar, cheese and onion, beef and mustard, spit roast steak, and basil and tomato.

25. Flying the Flag
A. MAN OVERBOARD
B. STEAL THE BOOTY
C. BLOW THE MAN DOWN
D. BOOTY OVERBOARD

26. Sky Signals
NO
MILK
LEFT
BRING
MORE.

27. On the Big Screen
MUTE YOUR PHONE

28. Team Talk
NEW YORK BAY

Glossary

clue A small piece of information that helps you find an answer.

criminal Someone who has committed a crime.

decode To work out a code to find the answer.

destination The place that someone is going to.

emoji A small picture used on a phone to show an idea or emotion.

hike A long or difficult walk.

ingredient Something that is used in a recipe to make something else.

jewels A valuable stone or crystal.

Morse code A code where the letters of the alphabet are changed to combinations of dots and dashes.

solution Answer.

talent A skill or natural ability.

Further Information

Books

Around the World in 80 Puzzles by Aleksandra Artymowska, Big Picture Press, 2017.

Creative Picture Puzzles by Sarah Lawrence, Arcturus Publishing, 2017.

Over 50 Secret Codes by Emily Bone, Usborne Publishing, 2015.

The Best Puzzle Book Ever by Andy Peters, Arcturus Publishing, 2017.

The Official Spy's Handbook, Usborne Publishing, 2014.

Websites

www.bbc.co.uk/cbbc/joinin/bp-can-you-find-it-puzzles
Have a go at these brainteasers on the BBC website.

www.cia.gov/kids-page/games/break-the-code/code-1.html
Check out the kids' page from the CIA and try to crack the codes!

Index

ARCTURUS

This edition published in 2020 by Arcturus Publishing Limited
26/27 Bickels Yard, 151–153 Bermondsey Street,
London SE1 3HA

Written by Kate Overy
Illustrated by Ed Myer and Graham Rich
Designed by Trudi Webb and Emma Randall
Cover designed by Ms Mousepenny

ISBN: 978-1-78950-301-2
CH006994NT
Supplier 33, Date 1019, Print run 9620

Printed in China